Dot on Top

Dot on Top

Daphne David

Michael O'Mara Books Limited

First published in Great Britain in 1999
by Michael O'Mara Books Limited
9 Lion Yard
Tremadoc Road
London SW4 7NQ

Dot on Top is published under licence from Paperlink Ltd
356 Kennington Road, London SE11 4LD.
Copyright © Paperlink Ltd 1999.

A CIP catalogue record for this book is available from
the British Library

ISBN 1-85479-466-3

1 3 5 7 9 10 8 6 4 2

Designed by Mick Keates
Formatting by Concise Artisans
Printed and bound in Great Britain by
Cox & Wyman Ltd, Reading, Berks.

'Please come down, Gavin.'
Begged Dot. 'I'm still the
woman you married. I've
just got some contact
lenses and had my hair done.'

After her promotion the
first thing Dot did was
change the way the
salesmen presented
their figures.

'Listen', snarled Dot to the uninvited charmer, 'I came in here to pick up a man, not a rash.'

Fifi was only a small dog but what she lacked in threatening stature she made up for in halitosis.

Dot liked to make it clear that, not only did she wear the trousers in her and Gavin's relationship, she owned them as well.

'There, there', cooed Dot, 'I know
you won't get another report
like this one and so Mummy
won't have to put you up
for adoption.'

Being a business woman Dot liked to cultivate a "tough guy" approach when it came to shaking on deals.

'So I forgot!' Said Dot
defensively. 'Anyway you
never put the sodding lid
back on the sodding
coffee jar!'

Things were a bit different
down at the bank now
Dot had some money
in her account.

Watching Punch and Judy made Dot forget all the cares of adulthood.

Dot started a small fire
in an attempt to attract
the sales assistants'
attention.

'I don't believe it!' Wailed Dot.
'Another sales rep scent marking his parking place!'

It was a rare moment when
Dot felt she could help
someone less fortunate than
herself. 'I could push you if
you like?' She offered.

Dot shuddered at the thought that dogs take after their owners. 'For God's sake Fifi shut your legs and get up'. She growled.

Dot didn't like Butch's style: 'Thanks, I will slip into something "a little more comfortable" – the front seat of my car. Goodbye.'

Jeremy obviously needed
sympathy, which, in a strange
way, made Dot want to
whack him.

Dot wasn't going to forgive Phillip's infidelity for a bunch of flowers. 'How lovely, she said, 'just wait here while I put them in some acid.'

'It's no use trying to befriend
my dog.' Said Dot. 'Fifi can
sense that I don't want a
relationship with you.'

'Yes it's another take away!'
Snapped Dot. 'Women who
cook for their men have
low self-esteem. Now shut up
and eat!'

"Dot acted swiftly when "Hunky Henry" called to see Jane: 'She's not here', purred Dot, 'she's down at the you-know-what clinic. Can I help you?'

Dot was never content having the last word in an argument. She liked to have the last plate as well.

Dot had the presence of mind to check her diary while Gavin was making amorous advances: 'The plumber's due in 5 minutes,' she panted, 'you'll be done by then, won't you?'

'Give us a break Dot,'
grunted her boss, 'even I know
you can't have period pains
3 fridays in a row.'

At School Sports Day, much
to her children's embarrassment,
Dot tried to "psyche out"
the opposition in the parents'
egg and spoon race.

Dot knew Robert wasn't drop-dead gorgeous. His eyes won her over: One was a "come to bed" eye, the other was an "I'll make the breakfast" eye.

Dot knew in her heart
there'd never be a good
or a bad time to end her
relationship with Bob —
so why prolong the agony?

'Goodness me, yes', chirruped Dot,
'of course you have a choice.
Either your girlie calendars
go or you go... or you both go.'

By switching her plant spray to MAX Dot could take out the neighbours' kids at *20* paces.

'It's my memento of Hugh.
His face forever set in
frying pan.' Sighed Dot.
'I made it the day he left.'

If Dot wanted promotion and to break through the "glass ceiling," she realised she had to throw her current boss out the glass window.

It wasn't the fact that
Gavin complained about
her faults that bugged
Dot — it was the way he
did it.

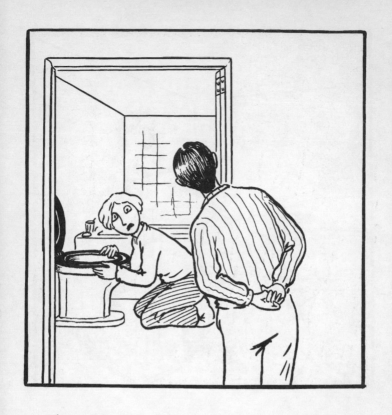

'I'm not bloody bulimic!'
Shouted Dot, 'I just O.D.'d
on some Champagne truffles
on the way home.'

Dot said a few well chosen words after the burial of her exercise bike: 'Good bloody riddance.'

'You want me to meet your mother!?' Gasped Dot.
'Oh Donald!... Hang on you're breaking up ... I'm losing the signal...'

'Yes, mother, I've persuaded Gavin to do something round the house,' said Dot, 'about 50 laps.'

Dot always gave a theatrical welcome to any new, bright young talent in the office ... until they cracked.

For the umpteenth time the computer told Dot it could not find the file she wanted, so she typed in one last command: 'piss off then.'

'Oh Bobby, you're a nice bloke,' sighed Dot, 'but I can't go to bed with a man who has hair like a sea urchin's fanny.'

'No, I didn't knit it myself,'
said Dot wearily, 'I slept
with the guy who designed it.'

'Remember, Arnold; it's a
woman's right to choose.'
Said Dot, 'so I will have
chocolate sauce on my
lobster.'

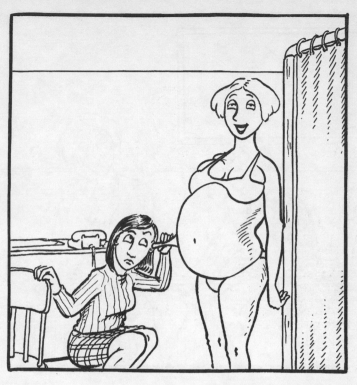

'Me? Having a baby? Don't
be silly, doctor,' tittered
Dot, slipping ever deeper
into denial.

Dot wished she'd never agreed to a drink with Cyril - it was like being sexually harassed by an over confident hamster.

Dot knew her power
dressing was making an
impact at work.

'I'm sorry,' said Dot, 'it's a throwback to my flower arranging days.'

'I know it's none of my business', said Dot, 'but would you mind not talking about your relationship. You're making my soup curdle.'

'No I don't want any replacement doors or windows,' growled Dot, 'and may I add that I can tell from your voice you're too stupid to get a proper job?'

'It'll grow back, Dorothy,'
said the doctor, 'but promise
me you'll never flambé a
banana in the nude again'.

'Take my advice', said Dot,
'stay at school until you're
about 85.'

'Jeepers weepers!' Thought Dot. 'Why the hell did I choose this restaurant to demonstrate my financial independence?'

Until she had them plucked
Dot had never realised
she had abnormally tough
eyebrows.

True to his word, "Romantic Rupert" tapped on Dot's window at midnight.

Dot complained to the store
   manager so much that
something was done about
the lack of parking space.

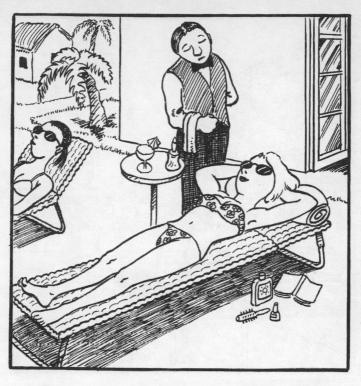

Dot rang for service. 'Ah Alphonse', she drawled, 'clear the table will you – I feel the need to watch somebody working.'

It took some negotiation, but Dot traded in her reward card points for the handsome lad behind the fish counter.

'This is serious, kids,' said Dot, 'where is Daddy? All the credit cards are in his shorts.'

'So just to recap: You love me, you want to take care of me, meet my every desire and have children with me.' Said Dot. 'Hmph! You've left out the bit where I die of over-work and boredom.'

'C'mon Dotty, you ol' sex machine!' Drawled Rupert. 'You said you were going to drag me back to your place and jump on me — so what's the delay?'

'Oh darling!...Darling, darling.
Mmmm darling... darling.'
Sighed Dot, as she desperately
tried to remember her
date's name.

Dot had to judge the local
body builders' competition.
'It's a tough decision', she
sighed, 'but I think no winners
this year as you're all
equally repulsive.'

"No woman", indeed!' Snarled Dot. 'I can tell you're lying — your lips are moving'.

'Jeezus!' snapped Dot, 'Would you two like to be alone?'

Dot remembered the young
man on the bicycle; he'd
stood her up once.
'Let me through, I'm a
doctor,' she lied.

'Really Gavin', whispered Dot, 'you're taking yourself a bit seriously... but then I suppose somebody has to.'

Occasionally, when Dot called at Gavin's office she had to remind his secretary who was No.1 woman in his life.

'You know, Doug,' said Dot 'If you just changed the way you dressed, talked, ate and stopped expecting me to be your mother, you'd be quite nice.'

'Yes, I can tell you the facts of life,' said Dot, 'women work and men get paid.'

Rich Ron didn't get the dirty weekend he expected from Dot, as she not only insisted on separate bedrooms but separate hotels.

Dot was itching for a fight. 'Tell me, Gavin, do I look fat in this dress?' she asked.

It was obvious Dot had a way with children.

Dot insisted on having a space of her own.

'Well don't worry,' said Dot,
"The woman of your dreams"
isn't into DIY, she's just
putting another notch in
the bedpost.'

Dot first smashed the washing-up with a hammer, then drove the car through the wall to make it look like an accident.

Dot only went to the shops
for a bar of chocolate.
But on the way home she
saw a dress that would
go with it...

'Of course we're not going to
have a 3 in a bed romp!'
Said Dot. 'One of you is
going to make the tea.'

Dot was in no mood for pretentious menus. 'This pan-fried pigeon with 12 herbs,' she said, 'could I have mine kettle-fried with 11 herbs?'

Dot talked to her plants
to encourage their growth.
'Another 6" by July, you
little bastards, or you're
compost!'

To the men in the office it was a "dog eat dog" world. But to Dot it was more than that; it was a "woman eat last chocolate biscuit world."

'Er... I'll have a salad too', said Dot. 'And maybe a side order of steak... and a few chips'.

Dot was ever wary
of colleagues encroaching
on her territory.
'John... get your finger off
my desk.' She snarled.

Finally Dot turned to the
guest on her right.
'You're ignoring me.' She said.
'Do you always take such
risks with your life?'

'No, no!' Insisted Dot. 'It's not modern art. I simply stuffed my husband in the fish tank after a row.'

Face down on the massage table was the only place Dot could break the health farm rules.

'Ok, I'll have a boob job'
said Dot, 'just as soon as
you have surgery to remove
that sofa from your
backside.'

'I need a roll-on deodorant
for my husband', said Dot,
'and I just wondered if
you had one in a bottle
rather than a penis.'

'And look at the expression on Pedro's face in this one!' Snorted Dot. 'And all that Sangria coming out of his nose. I'd just told him his wife was behind him'.

'Of course drugs are bad for your health', said Dot, 'because if you take them I'll find out and beat you into a senseless jelly'.

When her cleaner left to do a degree in physics, Dot shamefully forgot her sexual politics: 'The last thing the world needs is a bloody woman rocket scientist!' She squealed.'Stay here and look after me! Please!'

Dot had bought 2 bikinis
and a little silk number
for her surprise holiday
before Peter revealed it was
a week's whale watching
in New Zealand.

It wasn't really Dave's political stance that got on Dot's wick - it was just his stance.

It wasn't the fact that people gave her chocolates on her birthday that bothered Dot. It was the fact they expected her to share them that really got on her tits.

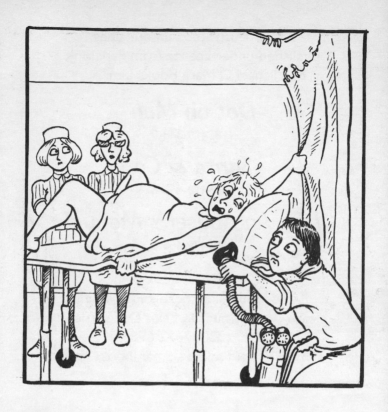

And as Dot's labour began in earnest she shouted those magical words every woman shouts to her mate at such an intense moment: 'I'll get you for this, you bastard!'